MW00889373

Ligers, and Tigons, and Bears– Oh My!

Copyright © 2021

All rights reserved.
No part of this publication, or the characters within it, may be reproduced or distributed in any form or by any means without prior written consent from the publisher.

For copyright permissions, school visits, and book readings/signings, email Info@everlycade.com.

Written by Everly Cade
Illustrated by Clare Tyas
Edited by Robin Katz
Formatted by Misty Black Media, LLC

ISBN Paperback 978-1-954211-07-0
ISBN Hardback 978-1-954211-06-3
ISBN eBook 978-1-954211-08-7

Library of Congress Control Number: 2021915562

Snapdragon
STUDIO

First Edition 2021
www.everlycade.com

Ligers, and Tigons, and Bears- Oh My!

Written by Everly Cade   Illustrated by Clare Tyas

This book belongs to

_____

This book is dedicated to my children.

Christian, Zachary, Grayson & Leah —

who bring color to my world

and make life beautiful!

♥ Mom

This book is dedicated to my three sons, Tom, Elliot and Isaac.

And to those fabulous people in my life that bring me smiles and strengh.

"Look for a smile in every day, even if some days you have to look a little harder.

Stand strong, believe in yourself... Chase those Dreams.

-Clare

We each are different. That is true.
There is no other just like you!

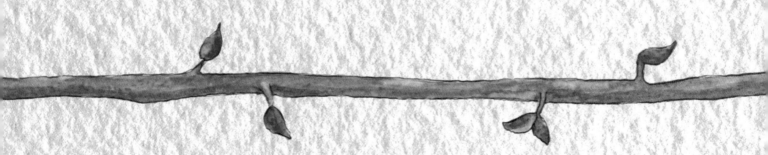

Your heart, your soul, your smile too—

are all the things that make you, YOU.

Across the world, both near and far
Are others, too— who shine like stars.

Let's meet new friends who are unique,

and we'll discover their mystique.

Daddy Lion and Mommy Tiger,
roll and play with baby Liger.

Mommy Tiger

Daddy Lion

Leo the Liger

Mister Goat and Missus Sheep,
love bleating with their baby Geep.

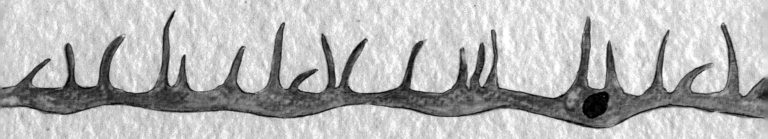

Polar Bear and Big, Brown Grizzly
love to feed their precious Pizzly.

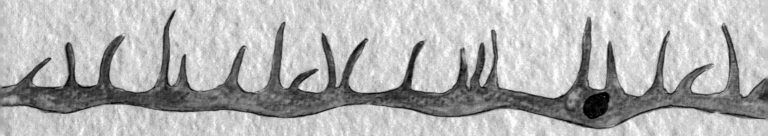

Polar Bear

Grizzly

Penelope the Pizzly

Mommy Zebra and Daddy Donkey,
zig and zag with little Zonkey.

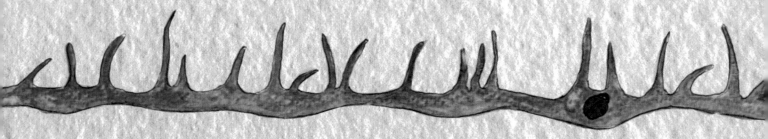

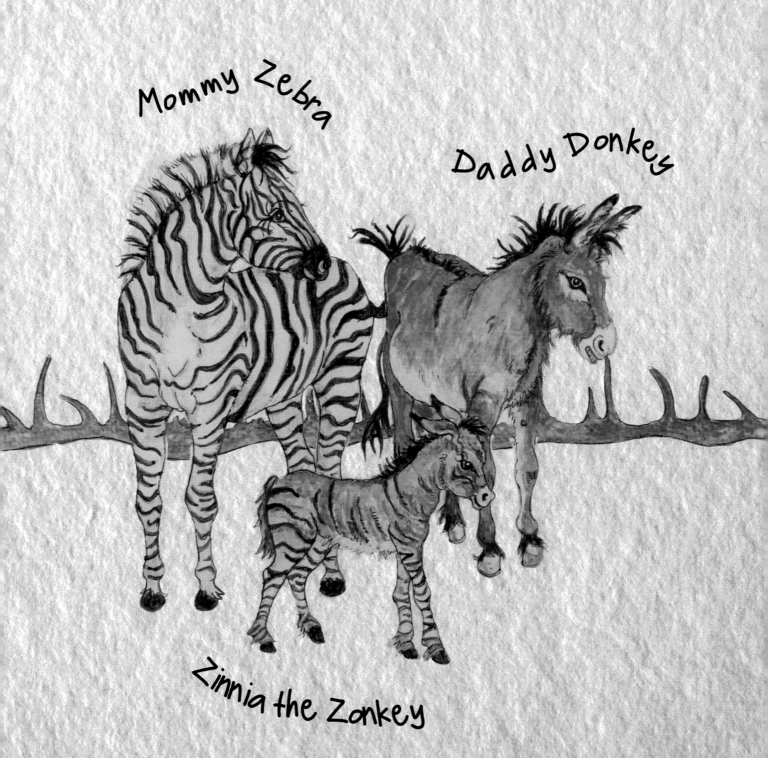

Narwhals and their Great Belugas

work on raising cute Narlugas.

Narwhal

Beluga

Nova the Narluga

Daddy Tiger and Mommy Lion,
toss and tussle baby Tigon.

Daddy Tiger

Mommy Lion

Talia the Tigon

Daddy Zebra and Mommy Horse,
both bray and neigh to tease their Zorse.

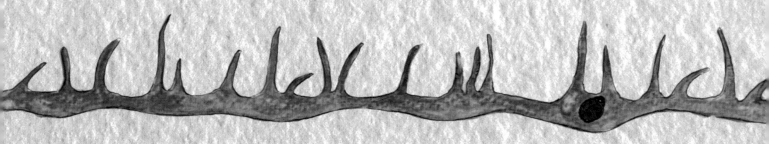

Mommy Horse

Daddy Zebra

Ziggy the Zorse

Sir Camel and his lovely Llama,
take long walks with little Cama.

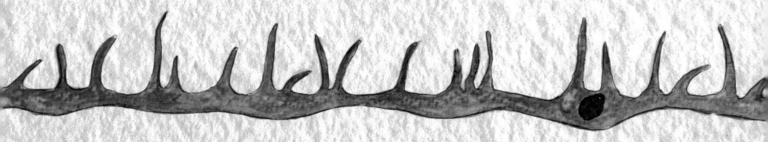

Born from love—they're like the sun.
They shine their light for everyone.

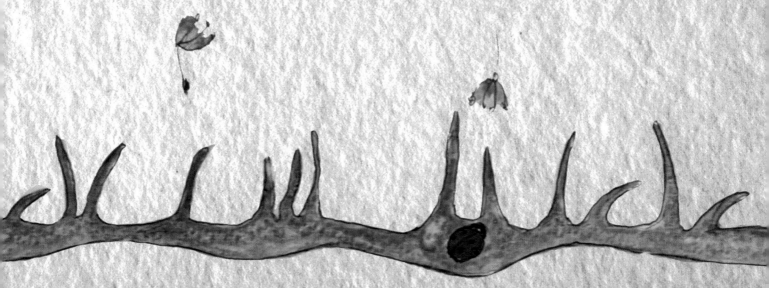

Ligers, and Tigons, and Bears—

Oh My!

Which one of these little animals

is your favorite?

Author Everly Cade looks at the world through the eyes of a child and finds magic and beauty in everything around her. Being inquisitive led her to write: Ligers, and Tigons, and Bears-- Oh My! the first book in the Wildly Wonderful Series. Look for more stories about extraordinarily rare but real creatures to be released soon. These will become your child's new favorite animals!!

She is an author, teacher, wife and proud Mother of four children; plus a fur baby. Everly and her family live in Upstate New York along the beautiful shores of Lake Ontario, a place that feeds her soul.

Everly's other books include: *The World is Mine - A Message of Love and Loss* and *What Do You Do? When the Life of a Loved One Has Come to an End*. Both of these poignant and comforting stories are written from the perspective of a child, and are a great way to initiate a difficult topic.

More about Everly can be found on her website www.everlycade.com.

Clare Tyas has been sketching and drawing for as long as she has been able to hold a pencil. She studied fine art and illustration and is renowned for her paintings and sketches inspired by animals encountered on her parents' farm and in the beautiful countryside of the UK's Yorkshire Dales, where she lives with her three sons. Her work captures the spirit and delightful personalities of the creatures she portrays; each has a special twinkle in its eye, and is painted to make you Smile! Clare named her company GingerArts . . . Art to make you Smile.

She also produces intricate townscapes and more abstract large-scale landscape paintings, primarily of locations in the North of England. In these, she captures the character and unique identity of places dear to her, whether working in great detail to depict houses, streets or daily life in her Townscapes.

Clare is a founding partner of Gingerbugs & Co, an independent gift shop in Ingleton, in the Yorkshire Dales, UK.

www.gingerarts.co.uk

Made in the USA
Middletown, DE
16 September 2021

48098065R00022